Rob's First Pet Care Book

written by Rob Domino
illustrated by Paulette Bogan

**McGraw-Hill
School Division**

New York   Farmington

You have in your hands the best pet care book I've ever written. I hope you'll buy my second book, too.

What if your pet has all its teeth, a healthy, cold nose, and doesn't bite much? Maybe you don't need this book. Too late! It's yours.

Rob

The first question about pet care is, "What pet do you care about?" Before you answer, you should know what pets look like.

Some pets are big and some are small. The big ones weigh more than the small ones. So if you plan to carry your pet around, pick a small one.

Some pets make lots of noise. If you love
noise, those are the pets for you.

Some pets need lots of care. If you're
lazy, don't get one of them. Get a goldfish.

Whatever you pick, follow this rule. Decide
what you want before you go to the pet store—
or you might end up with the wrong kind of pet.

Once you've decided on a pet, you'll have to remember what it looks like.

I can help. I've seen lots of people and pets. I can tell them apart, even from hundreds of feet away. Here's a clue—the pets are usually the tame ones.

You go to the store, but the pet you want isn't acting right. Even if the pet is a special price, keep searching. Try a different store.

At last you've got a pet. You must learn
to understand it. What is this cat saying?
Hint: "Feed me!"

Never feed cornflakes to a cat. They aren't good for the cat, and they cost too much. Find out what food your pet really needs.

And remember, your pet is an animal.
It must drink, too. Put out fresh water every
day. And give it a treat sometimes. But not
when it's bad. That would just confuse the
pet. Give yourself a treat instead.

Pets need exercise, too, but they might refuse to go to the gym. You need another way to keep your pet fit.

If your pet misbehaves, you can chase it a lot. Then you'll both stay fit and happy. A cheap toy helps. Give your pet one as well.

If your pet doesn't have a damp, cold nose, take it to the vet. If your pet does not have a nose, don't worry. A good pet care book can tell you what to do.

Your own nose should be warm and dry. If it isn't, have it checked out. But not at the vet.

As your pet gets older, it has different needs.
Change the food it eats. And change the litter!
(This really should be done quite often.)

Your pet might be a good parent, but only if it has babies. If that happens, you'll need more advice than this book gives. You'll need *Rob's Second Pet Care Book*. Buy it today!